KS2 SATs
Reading
10-Minute Tests

Rachel Lopiccolo

Schofield & Sims

Introduction

This book contains 22 bite-sized tests to give you practice in answering comprehension questions quickly. Each test contains a fiction, non-fiction or poetry text followed by between five and eight questions and is designed to be completed in 10 minutes. The questions are just like the questions you will need to answer in the SATs Reading paper in Year 6.

What you will need

- a pencil
- an eraser
- a clock, watch or stopwatch
- an adult to time you and mark the tests for you

How to use the book

Make sure that you are sitting in a quiet place where there aren't any distractions. Turn to **Test 1** on page 4. When you are ready to begin, ask the adult to start the timer. Read the text and then answer the questions.

Work through the questions in order. Try to answer every question. If you get stuck on a question, leave it and move on to the next one. Work quickly and try to do your best. Remember, this is not a memory test. You can – and should – refer to the text as often as you need to answer the questions.

When you reach the end of the test, stop and tell the adult that you have finished. The adult will mark your test. Then the adult will fill in the **Total marks** and **Time taken** sections at the end of the test.

Turn to the **Progress chart** on page 48. Write your score in the box and colour the chart to show this score. If you got some of the questions wrong, have another go at them before you look at the answers. Then ask the adult to check your work and help if you are still not sure.

Published by **Schofield & Sims Ltd**, 7 Mariner Court, Wakefield, West Yorkshire WF4 3FL, UK
Telephone 01484 607080
www.schofieldandsims.co.uk

This edition copyright © Schofield & Sims Ltd, 2019
First published in 2019
Sixth impression 2022

Author: **Rachel Lopiccolo**
Rachel Lopiccolo has asserted her moral rights under the Copyright, Designs and Patents Act, 1988, to be identified as the author of this work.

British Library Cataloguing in Publication Data
A catalogue record for this book is available from the British Library.

Extract from **Malkin Child: A Story of Pendle's Witches** by Livi Michael, published by Foxtail, an imprint of Litfest Publications. Extract from **Moonrise** (Warriors: The New Prophecy, Book 2) by Erin Hunter. Reprinted by permission of HarperCollins Publishers Ltd © 2005 Erin Hunter. Extract from **Tarka the Otter** by Henry Williamson, published by Puffin Books. © Henry Williamson Literary Estate. Extract from **Thirteen Hours** by Narinder Dhami. Published by Tamarind. Reprinted by permission of The Random House Group Limited. © 2015. Extract from **The Snow Sister** by Emma Carroll, Faber and Faber Ltd, 2007. Reproduced by permission of the publisher. Extract from **The Thief Lord**. Text copyright © Cornelia Funke 2000. Reproduced with permission of Chicken House Ltd. All rights reserved. Extract from **Dolphin Song** by Lauren St John, first published in the UK by Orion Children's Books, an imprint of Hachette Children's Books, Carmelite House, 50 Victoria Embankment, London, EC4Y 0DZ. Extract from **Journey to the River Sea** published with permission of Macmillan Children's, an imprint of Pan Macmillan, a division of Macmillan Publishers International Limited, copyright © 2001 Eva Ibbotson. Extract from **The Spook's Apprentice** by Joseph Delaney. Published by Bodley Head. Reprinted by permission of The Random House Group Limited. © 2004. Extract from **Minnow on the Say** by Philippa Pearce. Copyright © Philippa Pearce 1955. Reproduced by permission of the Licensor through PLSclear. Extract from **I Saw Three Witches** by Walter Ramal. Reproduced by permission of The Literary Trustees of Walter de la Mare and The Society of Authors as their Representative. Extract from **Pygmalion** by George Bernard Shaw. Reproduced with permission of The Society of Authors as agents for the Bernard Shaw Estate.

Design by **Ledgard Jepson**
Illustration by **Tamara Joubert (Beehive Illustration)**
Printed in the UK by **Page Bros (Norwich) Ltd**

ISBN 978 07217 1497 4

Contents

Notes for parents, teachers and other adult helpers

A pull-out answers section (pages A1 to A8) appears in the centre of this book, between pages 24 and 25. This provides answers to all the questions, along with guidance on marking the papers. Remove the pull-out section before the child begins working through the tests.

Test 1

Extract from *Malkin Child* by Livi Michael

It is the year 1612 and Jennet, who believes her family are witches, has been out gathering sticks. She meets up with her sister, Alizon, to walk home together.

It was later than we thought when we met up, and the trees were up to their usual stuff, murmuring and whispering to one another in the darkness. And if you got too close they'd touch your shoulders with their long, twiggy fingers. So me and Our Alizon stayed close to one another, holding hands, not speaking, in case anything was listening.

Soon as we got in, all the rest of the light drained off. Nothing was quite what it seemed. For instance, I nearly bumped into a hairy old man, and I was about to yell, when I saw it was only a tree stump covered with ivy.

All the trees had holes in their trunks, like open mouths.

We could hear the drip, drip, drip of rain on leaves and it sounded a bit like footsteps.

Pad, pad, pad.

Not human footsteps.

Alizon looked round fearfully and I shifted my bundle of sticks under my arm and prepared to run.

Something rustled through the bushes, first one side, then the other.

We moved away from where we thought the noise was, but it moved with us.

Pad, pad, pad, pad.

And behind us.

Rustle, rustle, rustle.

Then the whistling started.

It was like no whistling I'd ever heard before – a high-pitched, lonely sound that made it sound like it was hundreds of miles away, and at the same time right in front of us. Or just behind. Or to the left.

Just when we thought we'd worked out where it was coming from, another whistle joined it, coming at us from a different place, and then another.

My grip tightened on Alizon's hand. 'What is it?' I whispered, but she only shook her head, and her eyes were very bright.

When a fourth whistle started, we didn't say anything else – we ran.

1 In what type of location is the extract set?

....

1 mark

2 Who or what is described as having *long, twiggy fingers*? Tick **one**.

Alizon ☐   the narrator ☐   a hairy old man ☐   the trees ☐

1 mark

3 Look at the paragraph beginning *Soon as we got in…*
Find and **copy** a phrase that tells you it was getting dark.

....

1 mark

4 *Pad, pad, pad.*
Not human footsteps.
What effect do you think the author is trying to create with these lines?

....

....

1 mark

5 The narrator says that the trees were **murmuring**. Which of the following words is closest in meaning to *murmuring*? Tick **one**.

chatting ☐   mumbling ☐   talking ☐   shouting ☐

1 mark

6 Look at the first paragraph. **Find** and **copy one** example of a **metaphor**.

....

1 mark

7 How do you think Jennet and Alizon feel? Give at least **two** pieces of evidence from the text to support your answer.

....

....

....

2 marks

Total marks ....   Time taken ....

Test **2**

A Biography of Mo Farah

Mo Farah is famous around the world for being one of Great Britain's greatest-ever distance runners. He has broken numerous European, world and Olympic records and won many medals.

Mohamed Mukta Jama Farah was born on 23rd March 1983 in Mogadishu, Somalia. He moved to London at the age of eight with his family, following some time living as a refugee with relatives in Djibouti. On arrival in England, Mo could speak very little English but he could run fast; his talents were spotted by one of his school teachers who encouraged Mo to join a local running club. Mo did, although his ambition at that time was to play football for Arsenal.

At the age of 14, Mo won his first school title and five years later he won the European Athletics Junior 5000m race. However, it was another 10 years before he emerged as a talent on the world athletics stage.

Mo represented Great Britain in the 2008 Olympics in Beijing. He returned from China without any medals but in 2012, at the London Olympics, Mo made history by winning Olympic gold in both the 5000m and 10,000m races. His success in London earned him not only two gold medals, but also the honour of being awarded a CBE from the Queen. A postbox in his town was also painted gold in recognition of his achievements. He repeated the double-gold feat four years later at the Rio Olympics and his services to athletics have since seen him receive a knighthood.

In summer 2017, Mo announced his retirement from track-based athletics having won 10 gold medals at successive World Championships and Olympic Games and having also become the first athlete to win three long-distance doubles at successive World Championships and Olympic Games. He finished third in the 2018 London Marathon and announced that he is aiming to represent Great Britain in the marathon at the 2020 Tokyo Olympics.

Mo is a devout Muslim who believes his faith helps him to train and achieve his goals. He and his wife have four children, to whom he has dedicated each of his four Olympic medals.

---

1   Which **three** countries has Mo Farah lived in, according to the text?

....

1 mark

---

2   Look at the paragraph beginning *Mohamed Mukta Jama Farah was born…*
Find and **copy one** word that suggests Mo left the country of his birth because it was unsafe there.

....

1 mark

3 What did Mo initially want to be when he was older?

....

1 mark

---

4 After winning two gold medals at the London Olympics in 2012, what **two** honours did Mo receive?

1) ....

2) ....

1 mark

---

5 *He repeated the double-gold* **feat** *four years later at the Rio Olympics...*
What does the word *feat* mean in this sentence? Tick **one**.

achievement ☐   win ☐   award ☐   succeed ☐

1 mark

---

6 Who has Mo dedicated his Olympic medals to? Tick **one**.

his relatives in Djibouti ☐   his wife ☐

his school teacher ☐   his four children ☐

1 mark

---

7 Why do you think Mo might have decided to switch from track to road racing? Explain your answer using evidence from the text.

....

....

....

....

2 marks

Total marks ....   Time taken ....

Extract from *Moonrise* by Erin Hunter

The warrior cats have ventured into the mountains. There they have met a clan, Tribe of Rushing Water, who are under threat from a mountain lion, Sharptooth. The tribe believe that Stormfur has been sent to save them, so they send away the other cats and force Stormfur into Sharptooth's cave to banish him from their territory. The warrior cats have made the decision to try and rescue their friend.

A terrible shrieking broke out in the cave, slicing through the sound of the rain pattering around them and even the noise of the falls. Feathertail sprang to her paws; every hair on her pelt told her to flee as far from the cave as she could. Only the thought of the danger that Stormfur was in made her stay where she was.

"Come on!" Brambleclaw's voice was tense.

The rest of the cats stared at him in disbelief.

"Down there?" Crowpaw demanded. "Are you mouse-brained?"

"Think!" Brambleclaw was already bounding towards the cave entrance; he paused and swung around to face the apprentice. "With Sharptooth in the cave, no cat will notice us. This might be our only chance to get Stormfur out."

Without waiting to see if the others were following, he leaped down the rocks towards the path.

"I still think he's crazy!" muttered Crowpaw, but he followed all the same.

Feathertail scrambled down after them, her paws sliding on the wet rocks, her claws scraping painfully as she tried to keep her balance. She ran along the ledge behind the falls with barely enough time to be afraid of slipping and falling into the turbulent pool below. The screeching grew louder. Terror surged through Feathertail as she imagined what they would find inside the cave; Sharptooth might be sinking his fangs into Stormfur's neck at that very moment, clawing her brother's pelt and turning him into fresh-kill.

She skidded into the cave and halted just behind Brambleclaw. For a moment she could hardly make sense of what she was seeing. With the moon covered by clouds, the cave was almost dark; the huge shape of Sharptooth seemed to be everywhere at once, massive paws pounding on the floor as he sprang from wall to wall, blood splattered against his flanks and saliva dripping from his jaws.

1 What **three** sounds can be heard in the first paragraph of the extract?

....

1 mark

2 Why does Brambleclaw think his plan might work?

....

....

1 mark

3 Look at the paragraph beginning *"Think!" Brambleclaw was already…*
Find and **copy one** word that means 'a person who is learning a skill'.

....

1 mark

4 *Without waiting to see if the others were following, he leaped down the rocks towards the path.*
What does this sentence tell you about Brambleclaw's character?

....

1 mark

5 *…afraid of slipping and falling into the **turbulent** pool below.* What does the word *turbulent* tell you about the water in the pool? Tick **one**.

It is deep. ☐   It is rough. ☐   It is dark. ☐   It is cold. ☐

1 mark

6 Explain in your own words Feathertail's conflicting feelings in the first paragraph. Use at least **two** pieces of evidence from the text to support your answer.

....

....

....

2 marks

7 The scene in the final paragraph could **best** be described as… Tick **one**.

inspiring ☐   shocking ☐   satisfying ☐   jubilant ☐

1 mark

Total marks ....   Time taken ....

Test 4

A History of Titanic

She was hailed as the 'unsinkable' ship, but *Titanic* became infamous as the ship that sank on her maiden voyage after hitting an iceberg in the Atlantic, with the loss of over 1,500 lives.

Built in Belfast between 1909 and 1912, *Titanic* was the largest ship to have ever been constructed at the time and required the shipyard where she was built to be modified with the demolition of three existing slipways to accommodate her. She measured over 880 feet in length and 175 feet from the keel to the top of her funnels – the equivalent of an eleven-storey building.

Designed to be the pinnacle of comfort and opulence, *Titanic*'s first-class passengers had available to them a gym, swimming pool, libraries and luxurious cabins. Even the third-class, or steerage, passengers, whose accommodation was basic in comparison, could enjoy standards above those on other vessels at the time.

Her fateful voyage began in Southampton on 10th April 1912. From Southampton, *Titanic* collected passengers from Cherbourg in France and Queenstown in Ireland before heading out across the Atlantic. She was due to arrive in New York on the morning of 17th April. However, at 11.40 p.m. on 14th April, *Titanic* struck an iceberg, causing catastrophic damage to the starboard side. This led to five of the watertight compartments being flooded and the ship started to sink. The crew immediately began the evacuation of passengers on to lifeboats, following the protocol of women and children first. However, some lifeboats were lowered before being filled and there were not enough lifeboats for the number of people aboard.

At 2.20 a.m. on 15th April, *Titanic* sank.

Two hours later, 705 people were rescued by RMS *Carpathia*, aboard which they continued their journey to New York, where they arrived three days later.

Following the disaster, an inquiry was held to investigate what had happened, the legacy of which was an improvement in safety aboard all ships, including the requirement for sufficient lifeboats for all those aboard.

The wreck of *Titanic* still lies beneath the Atlantic and the disaster still interests people over 100 years later.

1   *Designed to be the pinnacle of comfort and opulence...*
What does this tell us about *Titanic*?

....   1 mark

2   How long should it have taken *Titanic* to reach New York?

....   1 mark

3 Number these cities from 1 to 4 to show the **order** in which *Titanic* was there.

Southampton	
Queenstown	
Belfast	
Cherbourg	

1 mark

4 Look at the paragraph beginning *Built in Belfast between 1909 and 1912...* What problem did *Titanic*'s size cause according to the text?

....

....

1 mark

5 Where were the survivors of *Titanic* taken and how?

....

....

1 mark

6 Look at the paragraph beginning *Her fateful voyage began...* **Find** and **copy one** word that means 'an accepted procedure'.

....

1 mark

7 Look at the paragraph beginning *At 2.20 a.m. on 15th April...* What effect do you think the writer is hoping to create by using a one-sentence paragraph here?

....

1 mark

8 What development in shipping did the sinking of *Titanic* lead to? Tick **one**.

ships needing to have enough lifejackets for all passengers ☐

ships being made watertight ☐

ships needing to have enough lifeboats for all passengers ☐ ☐

1 mark

Total marks .... Time taken ....

Test 5

Pipertown Council Offices
High Street
Pipertown
PP8 2RL

Little Piper Primary School
Cherry Blossom Lane
Pipertown
PP8 1EC

9th October 2019

Dear Councillor Downham

We are writing to you concerning the amount of rubbish that we are finding on the footpaths and in the river near our school. We are very unhappy about what appears to be an increasing problem.

At our school, we pride ourselves on helping the environment and on ensuring we 'reduce, reuse and recycle'. However, there are clearly people in our community who do not share our feelings towards keeping our local area tidy. We feel that these people need to be educated about how to care for our local area to prevent it from becoming an eyesore.

We have already made posters to put up along the footpaths reminding people not to drop their litter but we feel the council should also be doing more to stop this happening. We believe that one of the biggest causes of this problem is that there are no bins in the immediate vicinity of our school. We would like to request that a bin is installed along the path near the river and another one on the road outside school in the hope that it would encourage people to throw away their rubbish instead of dropping it as litter.

Are you aware of the terrible effects that litter can have on wildlife? The river is home to ducks, swans and fish who will be affected by the rubbish because they could ingest smaller pieces, leading to internal problems, or become injured by or entangled in larger items. We think this is unacceptable. Every day, groups of us go with our teacher along the paths and riverbank picking up what we can to keep the area tidy and the wildlife safe. We would like to suggest creating an action group of local residents who could take responsibility for doing this each day while the littering is still a problem.

We thank you for taking the time to read our letter and we hope that you will action some of the ideas we have suggested.

Yours sincerely
Class 6F

---

1 Look at the paragraph of the letter beginning *We are writing to you...*
Find and **copy** a phrase that suggests that littering is getting worse.

....

1 mark

---

2 *...there are no bins in the immediate **vicinity** of our school.*
Explain in your own words the meaning of the word *vicinity*.

....

1 mark

3 Look at the paragraph beginning *Are you aware of the terrible effects…*
Find and **copy one** word that means 'trapped'.

....

1 mark

4 Using information from the text, tick **one** box in each row to show whether each statement is a **fact** or an **opinion**.

	Fact	Opinion
Ducks, swans and fish live in the river.		
People need to be educated about how to care for the local area.		
The council should do more to stop littering.		
Every day, groups of children pick up the litter.		

1 mark

5 What **two** steps have the children already taken to change things?

1) ....

2) ....

2 marks

6 What steps do the children now want the council to take? Tick **two**.

Hand out fines to people who are seen dropping litter. ☐

Create groups of local people to go litter-picking. ☐

Install bins near the river and outside the school. ☐

Put up posters encouraging people to take their rubbish home. ☐ ☐

2 marks

Total marks .... Time taken ....

Test 6

Extract from *Tarka the Otter* by Henry Williamson

Earth trickled by the gap in the bank to the broken roots below. Voles were at work, clearing their tunnels, scraping new shafts and galleries, biting the rootlets which hindered them. An otter curled in the dry upper hollow of the fallen oak heard them, and uncurling, shook herself on four short legs.

Through a wood-pecker's hole above her she saw the star cluster of the Hunting Dogs as faint points of light. She was hungry. Since noon the otter had lain there, sometimes twitching in sleep.

The white owl alighted on the upright branch of the tree, and the otter heard the scratch of its talons as it gripped the bark. She looked from the opening, and the brush of her whiskers on the wood was heard by the bird, whose ear-holes, hidden by feathers, were as large as those of a cat.

The owl was hearkening, however, for the prick of the claws of mice on leaves, and when it heard these tiny noises, it stared until it saw movement, and with a skirling screech which made the mouse crouch in a fixity of terror sailed to the ground and clutched it in a foot. The otter gave but a glance to the bird; she was using all her senses to find enemies.

She stood rigid. The hair on her back was raised. Her long tail was held straight. Only her nose moved as it worked at the scents brought by the mist from the wood. Mingled with the flower odours, which were unpleasant to her, was the taint that had given her a sudden shock, causing her heart to beat quickly, for power of running and fighting if cornered: the taint most dreaded by the otters who wandered and hunted and played in the country of the Two Rivers – the scent of Deadlock, the great pied hound with the belving tongue, leader of the pack whose kills were notched on many hunting poles.

1 What is Deadlock?

....

1 mark

2 What **two** noises does the owl hear according to the text?

1) ....

2) ....

2 marks

3 What is described as being as *large as those of a cat*?

the owl's eyes ☐   the otter's eyes ☐

the owl's ears ☐   the otter's ears ☐

1 mark

4 Why does the otter pay no attention to the bird?

....

1 mark

5 *...which made the mouse crouch in a fixity of terror.*
What does this tell you about the mouse?

....

1 mark

6 Look at the final paragraph. How do you think the otter is feeling and why?
Explain your answer using at least **one** piece of evidence from the text.

....

....

....

2 marks

Total marks ....   Time taken ....

Extract from *Thirteen Hours* by Narinder Dhami

My life runs like clockwork. Nothing can go wrong, ever, because it could mean the difference between life or death. And I'm not joking.

When the school bell signals freedom at 3.45pm exactly, I always make a break for it. I run and I run, never stopping. Our house is 1.8 miles away, and I *must* be home by five minutes past four. No ifs or buts. There's no other way to make it on time except to run the whole way. Whatever it takes, I can't be late. *I will not be late*.

It doesn't matter where my last lesson of the day takes place. Wherever I am, I know the quickest way out of the school building. I learned the location of every classroom, staircase and exit on the first day I arrived at Hayesford Secondary School in September, just two months ago.

Last lesson this Friday is a double dose of French. Hiding away in a corner, still and silent, merging into the background, I keep my head down so the teacher doesn't notice me. It's what I'm good at. As usual, I watch the minutes tick away on the clock, and I count them down.

I have a routine, and today is no different. Three minutes before the bell, I slip books, pens and papers into my bag underneath the table. My jacket is already rolled up and bundled inside, placed there at lunchtime. I grasp the handles of my bag tightly. No one notices.

Come on, I think, clockwatching obsessively, counting down inside my head. Come *on*. The sixty seconds between 3.44 and 3.45pm seem like six hundred, as always.

Then the bell rings and I snap my laptop shut, although I leave it on the desk because it's not mine. It belongs to the school – I can't afford my own. I slide from my chair and before my classmates have even begun to pack away their stuff, I'm through the door.

Behind me, Mrs Kaye is still talking. "Have a good weekend, everyone, and don't forget, I want your homework in by –"

But I'm gone, expertly pulling my jacket from my bag and slipping it on as I speed down the corridor. Homework is the very least of my problems.

---

1   What does the narrator mean by *My life runs like clockwork*?

....

1 mark

---

2   What time must the narrator be home by each day?

....

1 mark

3 Number these things from 1 to 5 to show the **order** in which the narrator does them at the end of each school day.

runs down the corridor	
puts their books, pens and papers into their bag	
closes the computer	
leaves the classroom	
slides from their chair	

1 mark

4 What does the narrator say they are good at? Tick **one**.

following the same routine every day ☐

keeping their head down so the teacher doesn't notice them ☐

running home quickly ☐

never being late home ☐

1 mark

5 Why do you think the narrator says that the *sixty seconds between 3.44 and 3.45pm seem like six hundred*?

....

1 mark

6 **Find** and **copy one** word that means 'skilfully'.

....

1 mark

7 How does the narrator feel about school? Explain your answer in full using at least **two** pieces of evidence from the text.

....

....

....

2 marks

Total marks .... Time taken ....

Extract from *The Snow Sister* by Emma Carroll

Christmas Eve morning wasn't the best time to get a telling-off, yet Pearl Granger was about to get one. She had been outside in the snow for all of two minutes, when above her head a window opened and her mother's voice rang out.

"What in heaven's name are you doing, you daft child?"

Pearl flinched. "It isn't what it looks like, Ma."

What it did look like was a girl in a patched-up frock putting the finishing touches to a person made out of snow. And that person, with two pilfered pieces of coal for eyes and a turnip for a nose, was now wearing Pearl's sister Agnes's best shawl.

"Bring that back inside this instant, do you hear?" Ma said, and Pearl knew it wasn't the coal or the turnip her mother meant, though both were in short supply. Ma shut the window again with a slam.

Pearl sniffed back the tears. She wasn't going to cry, not when it was very nearly Christmas and the snow lay so thick and beautiful on the ground. Ever since she could remember, she'd loved the snow. So too had Agnes, and together they'd rolled in it, fought in it, shut their eyes and tasted it. Even without Agnes the snow still made everything seem better, like a clean sheet over an old mattress.

And Pearl was proud of her finished snow sculpture. The size of a real-life girl, it had a sharp face, a certain tilt to the head. With Agnes's shawl now in place – and with a good deal of squinting – it might almost be her sister stood before her.

Almost. But not quite.

With a sigh, Pearl removed the shawl and, holding it to her face, breathed in. Agnes's smell was of violets – the sweets, not the flowers. After she died, it had lingered in the house, as if she couldn't quite leave. Only when Ma packed Agnes's things in a tin trunk did the violet smell disappear. A year later, and though it was bad luck to keep them, all their mourning clothes were folded and stored inside the same trunk. Yet the blackness in their hearts proved more difficult to hide.

---

1   Who does Pearl hope the snow person will look like?

....

1 mark

---

2   Look at the paragraph beginning *What it did look like was a girl...*
Find and **copy one** word that means 'to have taken without permission'.

....

1 mark

---

3 Why is Pearl's mum cross with her? Tick **one**.

because she has stolen a turnip and some coal ☐

because she has taken her sister's shawl ☐

because she should still be in bed ☐

because she is getting cold playing in the snow ☐

☐
1 mark

4 Look at the fourth and fifth paragraphs. **Find** and **copy** a phrase that suggests Pearl and her Ma do not have much money.

....

☐
1 mark

5 Specifically, what smell reminds Pearl of Agnes?

....

☐
1 mark

6 *A year later, and though it was bad luck to keep them, all their mourning clothes were folded and stored inside the same trunk. Yet the blackness in their hearts proved more difficult to hide.*
What do these two sentences tell you about Pearl and her mother?

....

....

☐
1 mark

7 Why do you think Pearl wants to make the snow person? Explain your answer in full using at least **two** pieces of evidence from the text.

....

....

....

☐
2 marks

Total marks .... Time taken ....

The Perfect Paradise
Do you want the holiday of a lifetime?

Paradise Bay Resort is the perfect choice for all the family. Whether you desire rest and relaxation or all-out action, we are perfectly placed for the picturesque old town and quiet coves, as well as bustling waterfront resorts and popular waterparks. Or, if you don't want to stray far from your hotel room, our resort has everything on site you could wish for to make your holiday dreams come true.

Paradise Bay Resort is the number one choice for families like yours, offering:

★ three swimming pools for fun in the sun

★ two restaurants serving delicious local cuisine and international favourites

★ a relaxing spa – perfect for unwinding and forgetting about everyday life

★ live entertainment every night in our bar

★ our ever-popular kids club providing all-day fun for children aged 3 to 13

★ excellent accommodation in our 150 recently refurbished rooms

★ spectacular views of the sea from our premium rooms

I loved all the swimming pools and the food in the restaurant. At the kids club, I made lots of new friends and got to make jewellery, play volleyball and learn songs.
Jade, age 7, Sheffield

We have had the best holiday ever. Thank you Paradise Bay Resort for making all our dreams come true.
Mrs Barker, London

I will definitely bring my family back here again. The hotel is in the perfect location for the beach, for the golf courses and for visiting AquaSplashLand and the old town.
Mr Ali, Glasgow

Our five-star holiday destination is the number one choice with travellers on popular travel review websites and has been described as 'the perfect paradise' by leading travel journalists.

So, what are you waiting for? Don't delay! Make your booking today.

---

1 What type of visitor is the advertisement aimed at? Tick **one**.

children ☐   families ☐   older people ☐   men ☐

1 mark

2 Look at the paragraph beginning *Paradise Bay Resort is the perfect choice...*
Find and **copy one** word that means 'full of busy activity'.

....

1 mark

3 List **two** of the activities that children can do at the kids club.

1) ....

2) ....

2 marks

4 Using information from the text, tick **one** box in each row to show whether
each statement is a **fact** or an **opinion**.

	Fact	Opinion
Paradise Bay Resort is perfect for all the family.		
There are two restaurants in the hotel.		
There is live entertainment every night in the bar.		
Paradise Bay Resort is 'the perfect paradise'.		

1 mark

5 What techniques does the writer use to persuade the reader to visit Paradise
Bay Resort? Mention **three** techniques and give an example of each.

Technique	Example

3 marks

Total marks ....   Time taken ....

Extract from *The Thief Lord* by Cornelia Funke

Prosper and Bo are orphans on the run in Venice. They have been befriended by a gang of street children. Bo has just been confronted by a detective and is explaining to the children what happened, when he suddenly runs away.

Prosper, meanwhile, turned round and ran after Bo. He pulled him away from the gondolas so violently that Bo nearly fell over. Then he vanished with him into the next alley.

"Hey, Prosper, wait!" Scipio called out before chasing after them. He caught up with them after a few metres.

"What are you doing, running off like that?" Scipio scolded, holding on to his arm. Bo freed himself from Prosper's grip and stood next to Scipio.

"Come with me!" Scipio said and without another word he pushed the two of them into the nearest souvenir shop. Riccio, Mosca and Hornet squeezed in after them.

"Act as if you're looking at something!" Scipio whispered. The shop assistant looked at them suspiciously. "If that bloke on St Mark's Square really was that detective then it won't do any good just to run away," he said to Prosper under his breath. "With all those people around you'd never notice him following you!" He crouched in front of Bo and put his hands on his shoulders. "That Victor – did he ask you any questions?" he asked. "When you were feeding the pigeons back on the square?"

Bo crossed his arms behind his back. "He asked me my name…"

"Did you tell him?"

Hesitantly, Bo nodded.

"What else did you tell him, Bo?" Hornet whispered.

The shop assistant looked towards them more frequently now, but luckily a party of tourists came in and kept her busy for the time being.

"I don't remember," Bo mumbled and looked at Prosper. "Did Esther send the detective?" His lip began to tremble.

Scipio sighed and got up again. He looked at Prosper. "What does this detective look like?"

"But that's just it!" The tourists turned around, and Prosper immediately lowered his voice. "This time he looked completely different! He had no beard and he wore glasses, and I could hardly see his eyes because he wore a cap. I only recognised him because he ran away. He moves his shoulders in a strange way when he walks. Like a bulldog."

1   Look at the paragraph beginning *What are you doing, running off...*
Why do you think Scipio holds on to Prosper's arm?

....

2   *Hesitantly, Bo nodded.*
Why do you think Bo is hesitant?

....

....

1 mark

3   How did Prosper recognise the detective? Tick **one**.

He was wearing glasses and a hat. ☐   He had a distinctive beard. ☐

He was following Prosper. ☐   He had a distinctive walk. ☐   ☐

1 mark

4   Why do you think the shop assistant looks at them suspiciously?

....

....

1 mark

5   **Find** and **copy** a sentence that suggests Bo is upset.

....

1 mark

6   *He crouched in front of Bo and put his hands on his shoulders.*
What does this suggest about Bo?

....

1 mark

7   Where was Bo and what was he doing when he was asked his name?

....

....

2 marks

Total marks ....   Time taken ....

Test 11

Extract from 'The Very Merry Voyage of the Macaroni Man'

This figure here before you is a Macaroni Man,
Who is built, as you may notice, on a most ingenious plan.
His skeleton, I beg to state, is made of hairpins three,
Which are bent and curved and twisted to a marvellous degree.
His coat-sleeves and his trouser-legs, his head and eke his waist
Are made of superfine imported macaroni paste.
And if you care to listen, you may hear the thrilling tale
Of the merry Macaroni Man's extraordinary sail.
One sunny day he started for a voyage in his yacht,
His anxious mother called to him, and said, "You'd better not!
Although the sun is shining bright, I fear that it may rain;
And don't you think, my darling boy, you'd better take the train?"
"Oh, no," said he, "no clouds I see,—the sky is blue and clear,
I will return in time for tea—good-by, my mother dear."

Full merrily he started off, the day was fine and fair,
And to his great delight he found no dampness in the air.
You know if he gets wet, a Macaroni Man is spoiled,
And if he stands too near the steam, of course he may get boiled.
But our hero used precautions,—carefully he shunned the spray,—
And when the steam blew toward him, he just steered the other way.
Now, as the breeze was from the land, his course lay out to sea;
He sailed so far that he felt sure he would be late for tea.
He sailed, and sailed, and sailed, and sailed,—he feared the dew would fall—
He tried to turn,—but oh, that steam! it would not do at all!

Carolyn Wells

1   What **two** things is the Macaroni Man made from?

   1) ....

   2) ....

1 mark

2   How does the Macaroni Man travel on his voyage?

....

1 mark

KS2 SATs Reading 10-Minute Tests

Notes for parents, teachers and other adult helpers

KS2 SATs Reading 10-Minute Tests are short, timed tests designed to build speed and confidence.

The questions in the tests closely match the questions children will need to answer in the Key Stage 2 SATs Reading paper, which is taken in Year 6. As children work through the book, the tests get progressively more challenging.

It is intended that children will take around 10 minutes to complete each test.

How to use the book

Remove this pull-out section before giving the book to the child.

Before the child begins work on the first test, together read the instructions on page 2. As you do so, point out to the child that there is a target time of 10 minutes for completing the test.

Make sure the child has all the equipment in the list headed **What you will need** on page 2.

Be sure that the child knows to tell you clearly when they have finished the test.

When the child is ready, say 'Start the test now' and make a note of the start time.

When the child has finished, make a note of the end time and then work out how long they took to complete the test. Then fill in the **Time taken** section, which appears at the end of the test.

Mark the child's answers using this pull-out section. Each test is out of eight marks. Most questions are worth 1 mark. For questions worth 2 or 3 marks, follow the advice on whether to award 0, 1, 2 or 3 marks. No half marks can be awarded. Then complete the **Total marks** section at the end of the test.

Turn to the **Progress chart** on page 48. Encourage the child to write their score in the box and colour the chart to show this score.

Whatever the test score, always encourage the child to have another go at the questions that they got wrong – without looking at the answers. If the child's answers are still incorrect, work through these questions together.

If the child struggles with particular question types, help them to develop the strategies needed.

Ask them to complete the next test at a later date, once they have had sufficient time to practise any question types they found difficult.

For questions requiring longer written answers, examples of possible answers children may give are provided. Often, multiple answers are possible so the examples are not exhaustive. Providing your child has given a sensible suggestion and fulfilled the criteria for the question, they should be awarded the mark/s.

Answers

Test 1 (page 4)

1. in a wood or forest — **1 mark**
2. the trees — **1 mark**
3. the light drained off — **1 mark**
4. The author is trying to create tension/ make you wonder what is there. — **1 mark**
5. mumbling — **1 mark**
6. **Award 1 mark for either of the following:**
   - the trees were up to their usual stuff, (murmuring and whispering to one another)
   - (they'd touch your shoulders) with their long, twiggy fingers
7. **Award 2 marks for recognition that they are scared/frightened with reference to at least two pieces of evidence from the text.** For example:
   - They imagine things.
     - They imagine the trees murmuring and whispering.
     - They imagine the trees touching them with long, twiggy fingers.
     - They imagine a tree stump is a hairy old man.
     - They imagine the tree trunks have open mouths.
     - They imagine the dripping of rain on leaves is footsteps.
   - Their actions.
     - They stay close to one another and hold hands.
     - Alizon looks around fearfully.
     - Jennet grips Alizon's hand tightly.
     - They run away.
   - They hear noises and don't know what they are.
     - They hear something rustling in the bushes and are not sure what it is.
     - They hear sounds like footsteps and are not sure what is making them.
     - They hear whistling and are not sure where it is coming from.

   Award 1 mark for recognition that they are scared/ frightened with reference to only one piece of evidence from the text.

Test 2 (page 6)

1. **Award 1 mark for all three correct:** Somalia, Djibouti and England/Great Britain
2. refugee — **1 mark**
3. a footballer (for Arsenal) — **1 mark**
4. **Award 1 mark for both correct:**
   - He was honoured with a CBE.
   - A postbox in his home town was painted gold.

5. achievement — **1 mark**
6. his four children — **1 mark**
7. **Award 2 marks for suggesting a sensible reason why Mo might have decided to switch from track racing to road racing with at least one piece of supporting evidence from the text.** For example:
   - I think he decided to switch because he had been so successful at track racing. He had already won 10 gold medals at successive World Championships and Olympic Games.
   - I think he decided to switch because he wanted a new challenge. He has already broken numerous European, World and Olympic records and won many medals.
   - I think he decided to switch because he hopes to win a medal in the Olympic marathon. He finished third in the London marathon and hopes to represent Great Britain in the marathon at the 2020 Olympics.

   Award 1 mark for suggesting a reason without giving any supporting evidence.

Test 3 (page 8)

1. **Award 1 mark for all three correct:** (a terrible) shrieking, rain (pattering) and [water]falls
2. He believes his plan might work because, with Sharptooth in the cave, they will not be noticed by the other cats. — **1 mark**
3. apprentice — **1 mark**
4. Brambleclaw is brave/determined to rescue his friend, no matter the danger. — **1 mark**
5. It is rough. — **1 mark**
6. **Award 1 mark for each of the following points, up to a maximum of 2 marks:**
   - She is afraid ('every hair on her pelt told her to flee as far from the cave as she could').
   - She is brave/wants to protect her friend ('the thought of the danger Stormfur was in made her stay where she was').
7. shocking — **1 mark**

Test 4 (page 10)

1. It was very grand/had been designed to be the most luxurious ship.
   Accept similar wording to show understanding of the luxuriousness of *Titanic* using vocabulary other than *comfort* and *opulence*. — **1 mark**
2. seven days/from 10th to 17th April — **1 mark**

3 Award 1 mark for all four correct:

Southampton	2
Queenstown	4
Belfast	1
Cherbourg	3

4 The shipyard had to have three slipways removed for her to fit in. **1 mark**

5 The survivors were taken to New York aboard another ship (called RMS *Carpathia*). **1 mark**

6 protocol **1 mark**

7 to emphasise something sad and/or dramatic/ to shock the reader **1 mark**

8 ships needing to have enough lifeboats for all passengers. **1 mark**

Test 5 (page 12)

1 an increasing problem **1 mark**

2 the area around a particular place/close to/ near to/nearby **1 mark**

3 entangled **1 mark**

4 Award 1 mark for all four correct:

	Fact	Opinion
Ducks, swans and fish live in the river.	✓	
People need to be educated about how to care for the local area.		✓
The council should do more to stop littering.		✓
Every day, groups of children pick up the litter.	✓	

5 Award 1 mark for each, up to a maximum of 2 marks:
- They have made posters.
- They have been picking up litter every day.

6 Create groups of local people to go litter-picking. **1 mark**

Install bins near the river and outside the school. **1 mark**

Test 6 (page 14)

1 a great pied hound/a hunting dog **1 mark**

2 Award 1 mark for each, up to a maximum of 2 marks:
- the brush of the otter's whiskers on the wood
- the prick of the claws of mice on leaves

3 the owl's ears **1 mark**

4 She is looking out for enemies. **1 mark**

5 The mouse stops still because it is scared. **1 mark**

6 Award 2 marks for identifying how the otter feels with one piece of supporting evidence from the text. For example:
- The otter is feeling worried/scared because she can smell the scent of Deadlock, the great pied hound.

Award 1 mark for identifying how the otter feels without any supporting evidence.

Test 7 (page 16)

1 Their life runs very smoothly/with regularity/ exactly as planned. **1 mark**

2 five minutes past four/4.05 p.m. **1 mark**

3 Award 1 mark for all correct:

runs down the corridor	5
puts their books, pens and papers into their bag	1
closes the computer	2
leaves the classroom	4
slides from their chair	3

4 keeping their head down so the teacher doesn't notice them **1 mark**

5 because they are desperate to get home/they must be home by 4.05 so want to leave school as early as possible/when you are waiting for something time seems to go slowly **1 mark**

6 expertly **1 mark**

7 Award 2 marks for identifying that the narrator does not enjoy school with two pieces of supporting evidence from the text. For example:
- They feel trapped at school – they say the school bell signals freedom and they make a break for it.
- They can't wait to leave – they know the quickest way out of the building from any classroom.
- They count down the minutes until home time/ clockwatch obsessively.
- They have more important things to do – they say homework is the least of their problems.

Award 1 mark for identifying that the narrator does not enjoy school with only one piece of supporting evidence from the text.

Answers

Test 8 (page 18)

1. her sister, Agnes — **1 mark**
2. pilfered — **1 mark**
3. because she has taken her sister's shawl — **1 mark**
4. a patched-up frock/both [coal and turnips] were in short supply — **1 mark**
5. violet sweets — **1 mark**
6. **Award 1 mark for a sensible suggestion:**
   - They aren't ready to give away Agnes' clothes. They are still grieving.
   - They can't hide their sadness as easily as they can put away their mourning clothes.
7. **Award 1 mark for each sensible point made with a piece of appropriate supporting evidence, up to a maximum of 2 marks.** For example:
   - because Pearl and Agnes used to like playing in the snow together ('she'd loved the snow. So too had Agnes')
   - because Pearl remembers all the things she and Agnes used to do together in the snow/she misses playing with her ('together they'd rolled in it, fought in it, shut their eyes and tasted it')
   - because Pearl is still sad about her sister's death ('the blackness in their hearts proved more difficult to hide')

Test 9 (page 20)

1. families — **1 mark**
2. bustling — **1 mark**
3. **Award 1 mark for each, up to a maximum of 2 marks:**
   make friends, make jewellery, play volleyball, learn songs
4. **Award 1 mark for all four correct:**

	Fact	Opinion
Paradise Bay Resort is the perfect choice for all the family.		✓
There are two restaurants in the hotel.	✓	
There is live entertainment every night in the bar.	✓	
Paradise Bay Resort is 'the perfect paradise'.		✓

5. **Award 3 marks for any three from the following techniques, backed up with an example:**
   - Emotive language – for example, enjoy/ holiday of a lifetime/desire/relaxation/ picturesque/popular/dreams come true/ excellent/spectacular/love
   - Superlatives – for example, the best holiday ever/ the perfect location/ the number one choice/ the perfect paradise
   - Rhetorical questions – for example, Do you want the holiday of a lifetime? So, what are you waiting for?
   - Imperatives – for example, Don't delay! Make your booking today.

   Award 2 marks for any two, and 1 mark for any one.

Test 10 (page 22)

1. because he doesn't want him to run off again — **1 mark**
2. because he is worried about how the others will react when they know he has told Victor his name — **1 mark**
3. He had a distinctive walk. — **1 mark**
4. because they are whispering/they do not look like they are in the shop to buy something/she might think they are there to steal something because they suddenly squeeze into the shop, two of them being pushed — **1 mark**
5. His lip began to tremble. — **1 mark**
6. Scipio is taller than Bo/Bo is a child and Scipio is an adult or older child — **1 mark**
7. **Award 1 mark for each correct answer, up to a maximum of 2 marks:**
   - He was in St Mark's Square/the square.
   - He was feeding the pigeons.

Test 11 (page 24)

1. **Award 1 mark for both correct:**
   hairpins (three)
   (superfine imported) macaroni (paste)
2. in his yacht — **1 mark**
3. Accept any answer showing understanding of the word 'anxious'. For example: She is worried about him. — **1 mark**
4. It is sunny. — **1 mark**
5. **Award 1 mark for each, up to a maximum of 2 marks:**
   merrily and delight
6. **Award 2 marks for two sensible suggestions.** For example:
   - It might rain and he would get spoiled.
   - He might sail so far out he would be late back for tea.
   - He might get lost and not be able to find his way back.

   Award 1 mark for one sensible suggestion.

Test 12 (page 26)

1   covered   **1 mark**

2   22nd August (two days previously from 24th August)   **1 mark**

3   The cloud from the volcano made everything very dark.   **1 mark**

4   They were worried there may be a tsunami.   **1 mark**

5   **Award 1 mark for any two of the following and 2 marks for any three:**
ash, molten rock, pumice, poisonous gases, pyroclastic flow, ash-cloud deposits

6   **Award 1 mark for each point made, up to a maximum of 2 marks:**
They believed lots of people had died but hoped that there would be survivors.

Test 13 (page 28)

1   to make sure the sinister men are not there   **1 mark**

2   glittering black sea   **1 mark**

3   It is half the size and has gentle undulations rather than steep dunes.   **1 mark**

4   **Award 1 mark for both correct:**
- It is winter in Mozambique/there are very few guests at this time of year. (Do not award 2 marks for both of these as separate answers – one is an explanation of the other.)
- They may all be at dinner.

5   **Award 1 mark for each meaning, up to a maximum of 2 marks:**
- the outside/front of a building
- a deceptive appearance – for example, a disguise, a cover-up, fake, pretend, a sham, a show

6   **Award 1 mark for each of the following points, up to a maximum of 2 marks:**
- She has spent 11 days trying to escape an island that felt like a prison.
- She has ended up in a penal colony.
- She knows that despite being called Paradise, lots of suffering has happened there.

Test 14 (page 30)

1   mushrooms   **1 mark**

2   **Award 1 mark for all three correct:**
doubt, fear and panic

3   simile   **1 mark**

4   **Award 1 mark for all four lines drawn correctly:**

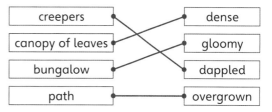

creepers		dense
canopy of leaves		gloomy
bungalow		dappled
path		overgrown

Note: encourage your child to join the answers with neat, ruled lines.

5   **Award 2 marks for acknowledging that Maia does not like the Carters (or has negative feelings towards them) with two pieces of supporting evidence from the text.** For example:
- She describes them as beastly.
- She says she is glared at by the twins.
- She describes the bungalow as gloomy (suggesting that she does not like living with them there).

Award 1 mark if only one piece of supporting evidence from the text is given.

6   **Award 2 marks for demonstrating an understanding that Maia's feelings are positive to begin with but become negative by the end of the extract, with at least two pieces of supporting evidence from the text.** For example:
- At the start she likes the jungle and comments on how beautiful it is, but as she becomes lost she feels it is an enemy.
- To begin with she is happy because she finds the jungle beautiful but by the end she feels doubt, fear and panic and agrees with the Carters that the jungle is the enemy.

Award 1 mark if only one piece of supporting evidence from the text is given.

Test 15 (page 32)

1   (about) five million   **1 mark**

2   delicacies   **1 mark**

3   The separate parts of Italy were joined together/Sicily became a part of the rest of Italy. (Accept any answer that demonstrates an understanding of the meaning of unification.)   **1 mark**

4   **Award 1 mark for any two correct:**
its own flag, its own saints and feast days, its own dialect

5   **Award 1 mark for both correct:**
agriculture and tourism

Answers

Test 15 (page 32) continued

6 **Award 1 mark for all four correct:**

	True	False
Sicily's climate is dry year-round.		✓
Mount Etna is a dormant volcano.		✓
Sicily's capital, Palermo, was formed after unification with Italy.		✓
Wales is smaller than Sicily.	✓	

7 **Award 1 mark for each reason with evidence from the text, up to a maximum of 2 marks:**
- The climate is mild year-round.
- The island has an interesting history.
- The island has spectacular examples of architecture.
- to see Mount Etna
- to visit the churches/cathedrals
- Palermo (or specifically Palazzo dei Normanni, Palermo Cathedral or Teatro Massimo)
- to sample the food

Test 16 (page 34)

1 happy **1 mark**

2 his half-sister (Do not accept 'sister'.) **1 mark**

3 They had been for a picnic (to the wood where the waterfall was). **1 mark**

4 **Award 1 mark for all four correct:**
stout, old, good and quiet

5 to imply they have a simple life/
to suggest they are ordinary **1 mark**

6 because they whisper together **1 mark**

7 **Award 2 marks for recognising that he enjoys it (accept any answer that indicates the relationship is positive/happy) with two pieces of evidence from the text.** For example:
- [She] was all the mother he had ever known.
- He had never envied other boys their mothers.
- Helen was so kind and clever and dear.
- She gave up almost all her time to him.
- She taught him all the lessons he learned.
- She played with him, inventing the most wonderful new games and adventures.
- Every morning when Philip woke he knew that he was waking to a new day of joyous and interesting happenings.

Award 1 mark for recognising that he enjoys it with only one piece of evidence from the text.

Test 17 (page 36)

1 drizzle **1 mark**

2 in an abandoned cow shed **1 mark**

3 moist **1 mark**

4 Accept an answer that implies he is curious about what to expect but is worried about what he would be told/he wants to know what might happen but feels he is better off not knowing. **1 mark**

5 "I bring all my new apprentices to this old house on their first night so I can find out what they're made of." **1 mark**

6 **Award 1 mark for each point made, up to a maximum of 3 marks:**
- The house is number 13 – an unlucky number (and possibly a sign that something bad may happen).
- The curtains are yellow and covered with cobwebs.
- The house is the haunted house that the narrator's master warned him about.
- The room is described as being empty, dark and damp.
- The flickering candle might go out at any second.
- The narrator says, 'What I saw was bad enough, but what he said was even worse.'
- The Spook says, 'At midnight … face whatever it is that's lurking there.'
- The narrator is described as being too scared and his top lip is trembling.

Test 18 (page 38)

1 calmly/serenely (or a similar word) **1 mark**

2 a boat **1 mark**

3 He does not believe they are called Smith/ telling the truth. **1 mark**

4 exasperation **1 mark**

5 **Award 2 marks for an answer that includes both points, or 1 mark for an answer that includes only one point:**
He is determined to find a way to achieve his plan whatever it takes. He realises it is difficult, which is why there is effort in his voice.

6 **Award 1 mark for showing understanding of how they feel.** For example:
They are suspicious/do not understand what the people's plans are.

Award another mark for an appropriate piece of evidence from the text. For example:
'there was at first a long and thoughtful silence'

Test 19 (page 40)

1. **Award 1 mark for each point, up to a maximum of 2 marks:**
   - They bow down (like barley).
   - They mount their brooms.

2. They are attacked by a hawk/A hawk ends their song.   **1 mark**

3. The witches are turned into bushes in the moonlight/They become bushes with red flowers on them.   **1 mark**

4. **Award 1 mark for both correct:**
   It flew fast and straight (like an arrow).

5. **Award 1 mark for showing understanding of both *concealed* and *grim*.** For example:
   Their ugly faces were hidden.

6. **Award 1 mark for three lines drawn correctly or 2 marks for all five lines drawn correctly:**

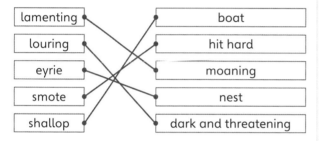

Test 20 (page 42)

1. three (evaporation, condensation and precipitation)   **1 mark**

2. **Award 1 mark for all four correct:**
   rain, sleet, hail and snow

3. **Award 1 mark for two lines drawn correctly or 2 marks for all four lines drawn correctly:**

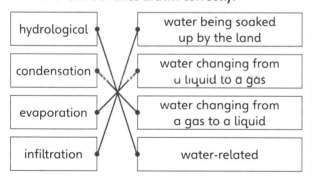

4. to make the reader think/to draw the reader in/ to encourage the reader to carry on reading   **1 mark**

5. water/liquid/moisture   **1 mark**

6. **Award 1 mark for each sensible point made, up to a maximum of 2 marks.** For example:
   - They are trying to warn people about the effects of global warming on the water cycle and how this will affect life on Earth.
   - The writer wants the reader to think about the changes affecting the world and what can be done about them.

Test 21 (page 44)

1. flashing fiercely   **1 mark**

2. **Award 1 mark for both correct:**
   He was mild. He was having difficulty making his way along the street.

3. feebly   **1 mark**

4. three (Phil, his step-mother and his step-brother, Jonas)   **1 mark**

5. wrathfully   **1 mark**

6. **Award 3 marks for two impressions, at least one with evidence.** For example:

Impression	Evidence
He is mischievous/ sneaky.	Phil heard a chuckling laugh.
He wanted to hurt Phil.	The snowball was hard. The snowball caused Phil considerable pain. Phil had no doubt that it was intentional.
He is unkind/cruel/ mean.	His spite got the better of his prudence. His eyes gleamed with malice.
He was disappointed that he was caught.	His freckled face showed a degree of dismay. He had not calculated on discovery.
He was cowardly.	He runs away from Phil when discovered. Fear winged his steps.

Award 2 marks for two impressions without evidence, or one impression with evidence. Award 1 mark for one impression without evidence.

Answers

Test 22 (page 46)

1 It is impossible to get a cab. **1 mark**

2 because of a sudden rain shower/
the weather **1 mark**

3 Award 1 mark for all four correct:

	True	False
Freddy is thirty years old.		✓
The scene takes place in Covent Garden.	✓	
It is summertime.	✓	
The lady, her daughter and Freddy are smartly dressed.	✓	

4 gumption **1 mark**

5 The text in brackets gives instructions for the actors/is not to be said by the actors. **1 mark**

6 **Award 1 mark for identifying how they feel about Freddy.** For example:
They think he hasn't tried hard enough.

Award 1 additional mark for each piece of supporting evidence from the text, up to a maximum of 2 additional marks. For example:

- The daughter says he has no gumption.
- They say he hasn't tried.
- They say that other people have managed to get cabs.
- The mother says he is helpless.

This book of answers is a pull-out section from **KS2 SATs Reading 10-Minute Tests.**

Published by **Schofield & Sims Ltd**, 7 Mariner Court, Wakefield, West Yorkshire WF4 3FL, UK
Telephone 01484 607080
www.schofieldandsims.co.uk

This edition copyright © Schofield & Sims Ltd, 2019
First published in 2019
Sixth impression 2022

Author: **Rachel Lopiccolo**
Rachel Lopiccolo has asserted her moral rights under the Copyright, Designs and Patents Act, 1988, to be identified as the author of this work.

British Library Cataloguing in Publication Data
A catalogue record for this book is available from the British Library.

All rights reserved. No part of this publication may be reproduced, stored in a retrieval system, or transmitted in any form or by any means, electronic, mechanical, photocopying, recording or otherwise, without either the prior permission of the publisher or a licence permitting restricted copying in the United Kingdom issued by the Copyright Licensing Agency Ltd.

Design by **Ledgard Jepson**
Printed in the UK by **Page Bros (Norwich) Ltd**

ISBN 978 07217 1497 4

3 In your own words, describe how the Macaroni Man's mother feels about his plans to travel.

....

....

1 mark

4 What is the weather like when the Macaroni Man sets off on his voyage?

Tick **one**.

It is snowing. ☐

It is raining. ☐

It is sunny. ☐

It is foggy. ☐

1 mark

5 **Find** and **copy two** words from the second verse that suggest that the Macaroni Man is happy about setting off on his voyage.

1) ....

2) ....

2 marks

6 What do you think might happen to the Macaroni Man next?

Mention **two** things.

....

....

....

....

2 marks

Total marks .... Time taken ....

The Roman Herald

29th August 79AD

Deadly Disaster!

Disaster has struck the cities of Herculaneum and Pompeii after Mount Vesuvius erupted in spectacular fashion last week.

On 24th August, Vesuvius sent forth a deadly cloud of ash, molten rock, pumice and poisonous gases which spewed down into the valleys, destroying everything in its path. Initial reports suggest that the two towns appear to have been completely destroyed, enveloped under a combination of pyroclastic flow and ash-cloud deposits.

Eye witnesses report having seen terrified citizens cowering in buildings and others desperately trying to make their way to boats on the coast in the hope of escaping the oncoming terror as the horror unfolded.

The nightmare began two days previously at approximately 1 p.m., when Vesuvius erupted violently, sending pumice high into the air. The pyroclastic flows which then headed down towards the town the following day were described as rapid, dense and very hot and have reportedly destroyed everything in their paths.

Pliny the Younger witnessed the terrifying events from across the Bay of Naples and described the scene: "Broad sheets of flame were lighting up many parts of Vesuvius; their light and brightness were the more vivid for the darkness of the night ... it was daylight now elsewhere in the world, but there the darkness was darker and thicker than any night."

Rescue committees have been organised from nearby towns, with the intention of using boats to reach the coastal areas. However, the fear of a tsunami has deterred some from joining in the rescue efforts.

Local government sources fear that the death toll may be catastrophic, but there is still hope that many citizens may have survived by escaping the destruction of their towns or by finding adequate shelter from the devastation.

1   ...*enveloped* under a combination of pyroclastic flow and ash-cloud deposits.
Which of the following words is closest in meaning to *enveloped*? Tick **one**.

crushed ☐   devastated ☐   destroyed ☐   covered ☐   ☐

1 mark

2   According to the report, when did the eruption begin?

.... ☐

1 mark

3   Explain what Pliny the Younger meant by "*it was daylight now elsewhere
in the world, but there the darkness was darker and thicker than any night.*"

.... ☐

1 mark

4   Why were some people put off joining in the rescue effort?

.... ☐

1 mark

5   Name **three** things caused by the eruption that were dangerous to
the towns.

1) ....

2) ....

3) .... ☐

2 marks

6   According to the report, what did the local government believe the
outcome of the eruption may be? Explain in your own words.

....

....

.... ☐

2 marks

Total marks ....   Time taken ....

Test **13**

An extract from *Dolphin Song* by Lauren St John

Having survived a shipwreck in shark-infested waters during a school trip, Martine and Ben have escaped from the island they found themselves upon by attracting the attention of a mysterious boat skipper. They have been taken to another island upon which they hope to find help to get home.

They set off towards the buildings, the sand squeaking under their bare feet. The island was about half the size of Dugong, with gentle undulations rather than steep dunes, so they decided to follow the glittering black sea all the way round and approach the building from the back. That way they could be sure that the sinister men weren't in sight before showing themselves.

"For a hotel, there don't seem to be too many lights on," Ben commented, as they peered between the wind-twisted trunks of some pine trees thirty minutes later.

"It is winter in Mozambique," Martine pointed out. "Perhaps there are very few guests at this time of the year, or perhaps they're all at dinner."

They waited a little while longer before venturing out into the open. It was only then, gazing up at the double-storey block of rooms and the forbidding façade of the hotel itself, its vast, curving terrace suspended over the ocean, they saw that that's all it was: a façade. A ruined shell. Not only was it unoccupied, it looked as if it had been that way for at least thirty years. The civil war or something else – mismanagement perhaps – had driven away the tourists.

Martine didn't know whether to cry or fly into a rage born of total despair. For eleven days she and the others had been trying to escape their island prison, only to end up here: the penal colony Alberto had told her about. She could still hear him saying, "Over the years, Santa Carolina has been a playground for wealthy tourists. They call it Paradise, but oh, Miss Martine, if only they knew what that paradise has seen: hundreds of hungry, suffering prisoners, tormented beyond what any man could endure, then taken to Death Island to be swallowed by the sea."

1 Why do Ben and Martine decide to approach the building from the back?
Tick **one**.

because there are more lights on that side of the building ☐

to make sure the sinister men are not there ☐

because the sand is difficult to walk on ☐

to surprise the sinister men ☐ ☐

1 mark

2   Look at the paragraph beginning *They set off towards the buildings...*
Find and **copy** a phrase that tells you it is night-time.

....

1 mark

3   How is this island different from the island of Dugong? Mention **two** things.

....

....

1 mark

4   What **two** possible reasons are given for the hotel not having many lights on?

1) ....

2) ....

1 mark

5   Look at the paragraph beginning *They waited a little while longer before venturing out...*
What are the **two** meanings of *façade*?

1) ....

2) ....

2 marks

6   Look at the final paragraph. Explain in your own words why Martine doesn't know *whether to cry or fly into a rage born of total despair*.

....

....

....

2 marks

Total marks ....   Time taken ....

Test **14**

An extract from *Journey to the River Sea* by Eva Ibbotson

Maia, an orphan, has been sent to live in the Brazilian jungle. Unhappy that the family she lives with has gone to the theatre and left her at home, she decides to try to make her own way into town.

Away from the compound, the great trees grew more thickly; dappled creepers wound round the trunks searching for the light; a scarlet orchid, hanging from a branch, glowed like a jewel in a shaft of the sun.

"Oh, but it is beautiful!" she said aloud, and drew the damp, earthy, slightly rotten smell into her lungs.

But it was a mistake to be so rapt about the beauty of nature because the path was not quite as simple as it had appeared on the map. She knew she had to keep the sun on her right; but the sun could not be relied upon; sometimes the canopy of leaves was so dense that she seemed to be walking in twilight. And the streams kept branching … She stayed beside the widest of them, but the path made by the rubber-gatherers was overgrown; she stumbled over roots of trees, trod on strange fungi, orange and mauve … Sometimes a smaller stream cut across her path and she had to jump it or paddle. Once something ran through the trees ahead of her, a grey snuffling creature …

She couldn't have told the exact moment at which she knew she was lost. First there was just doubt, as she took one path rather than another. Then doubt became fear and fear became panic, and she had to take deep breaths to stop herself from crying out. At the same time the clouds began to cover the sun. Even those rays of light she had had to steer by had gone.

They're right, the beastly Carters; the jungle is our enemy, she thought. Why didn't I listen? She would have done anything to be back in the gloomy bungalow eating tinned beetroot and being glared at by the twins. Trying to pull herself together, she walked faster. The stream she was following was quite big; a river really and the current was fast: it must lead to Manaus.

Blinking away tears, she trudged on. Then her foot caught in a liana, a long branch hanging like a rope from the top of a tree, and she fell.

---

1 What are described as *orange and mauve*? Tick **one**.

snakes ☐ mushrooms ☐ trees ☐ orchids ☐

☐
1 mark

---

2 Which **three** emotions does Maia feel when she becomes lost?

....

☐
1 mark

3 *...a scarlet orchid, hanging from a branch, glowed like a jewel in a shaft of the sun.*

What is this an example of? Tick **one**.

simile ☐   metaphor ☐   alliteration ☐   personification ☐   ☐

1 mark

4 Draw lines to match the features of the jungle to the description.

creepers	•	•	dense
canopy of leaves	•	•	gloomy
bungalow	•	•	dappled
path	•	•	overgrown

☐ 1 mark

5 Look at the paragraph beginning, *They're right, the beastly Carters...*

What does Maia think about the Carter family? Use **two** pieces of evidence from the text to support your answer.

....

....

....

☐ 2 marks

6 How does Maia's opinion of the jungle change in the extract? Explain your answer using at least **two** pieces of evidence from the text.

....

....

....

....

☐ 2 marks

Total marks ....   Time taken ....

Test 15

The Island of Sicily

Sicily, an island in the Mediterranean Sea off the south-western most point of Italy, is separated from the Italian mainland by the Strait of Messina. It covers an area of just under 10,000 square miles, making it slightly larger than Wales. Sicily has a population of about five million.

The climate is mild year-round with high temperatures in summer and heavy rainfalls in winter, making it suitable for agriculture – particularly the growing of olives, lemons, oranges, grapes, tomatoes and wheat. The economy is predominantly based around such agriculture, as well as tourism.

The island has had an interesting history, having been inhabited or ruled by Phoenicians, Greeks, Romans, Arabs, Normans and Spanish amongst others – all of whom have left their mark on the place and the people of today.

Although now a part of Italy following the unification of 1861, Sicily maintains a proudly independent sense of identity, having its own distinct flag, its own saints and feast days and its own dialect which is still spoken by older generations in some parts of the island.

The island is now famous for its spectacular examples of Roman, Greek and Moorish architecture with sights such as Agrigento, Taormina and Syracuse being popular with the hundreds of thousands of tourists who visit the island every year. Another popular tourist attraction is Mount Etna, the tallest active volcano in Europe.

The capital, Palermo, was first formed in 700BC by the Phoenicians who named it Ziz, meaning flower. It is a popular place for tourists to visit, home to numerous churches and cathedrals, the most famous and spectacular of which is Palermo Cathedral. Other popular attractions in the city include Palazzo dei Normanni (the Norman Palace) and the Opera House, Teatro Massimo.

Sicily is also famous for a number of popular foods, most of which can be bought from the bustling street markets of its towns and cities. One of the most famous delicacies is arancini (meaning little oranges because of their colour and shape). These are balls of rice typically filled with meat and peas, then coated in breadcrumbs and deep-fried. Another popular Sicilian food is cannoli – a sweet dish made from fried pastry filled with ricotta cheese.

1 According to the text, approximately how many people live in Sicily?

....

1 mark

2 **Find** and **copy one** word that means 'extremely tasty food'.

....

1 mark

3 Explain in your own words what happened in 1861.

....

....

1 mark

4 According to the text, how does Sicily maintain a sense of its own identity? Mention **two** things.

1) ....

2) ....

1 mark

5 According to the text, what are the **two** main ways in which Sicily earns money?

1) ....

2) ....

1 mark

6 Tick each statement to say whether it is **true** or **false**.

	True	False
Sicily's climate is dry year-round.		
Mount Etna is a dormant volcano.		
Sicily's capital, Palermo, was formed after unification with Italy.		
Wales is smaller than Sicily.		

1 mark

7 Suggest **two** reasons, giving evidence from the text, why people might visit Sicily.

....

....

....

2 marks

Total marks .... Time taken ....

Test 16

An extract from *The Magic City* by E. Nesbit

Philip Haldane and his sister lived in a little red-roofed house in a little red-roofed town. They had a little garden and a little balcony, and a little stable with a little pony in it – and a little cart for the pony to draw; a little canary hung in a little cage in the little bow-window, and the neat little servant kept everything as bright and clean as a little new pin.

Philip had no one but his sister, and she had no one but Philip. Their parents were dead, and Helen, who was twenty years older than Philip and was really his half-sister, was all the mother he had ever known. And he had never envied other boys their mothers, because Helen was so kind and clever and dear. She gave up almost all her time to him; she taught him all the lessons he learned; she played with him, inventing the most wonderful new games and adventures. So that every morning when Philip woke he knew that he was waking to a new day of joyous and interesting happenings. And this went on till Philip was ten years old, and he had no least shadow of a doubt that it would go on for ever. The beginning of the change came one day when he and Helen had gone for a picnic to the wood where the waterfall was, and as they were driving back behind the stout old pony, who was so good and quiet that Philip was allowed to drive it. They were coming up the last lane before the turning where their house was, and Helen said:

'To-morrow we'll weed the aster bed and have tea in the garden.'

'Jolly,' said Philip, and they turned the corner and came in sight of their white little garden gate. And a man was coming out of it – a man who was not one of the friends they both knew. He turned and came to meet them. Helen put her hand on the reins – a thing which she had always taught Philip was *never* done – and the pony stopped. The man, who was, as Philip put it to himself, 'tall and tweedy,' came across in front of the pony's nose and stood close by the wheel on the side where Helen sat. She shook hands with him, and said, 'How do you do?' in quite the usual way. But after that they whispered. Whispered! And Philip knew how rude it is to whisper, because Helen had often told him this. He heard one or two words, 'at last,' and 'over now,' and 'this evening, then.'

1 ...*he was waking to a new day of **joyous** and interesting happenings.*
What does the word *joyous* mean in this sentence? Tick **one**.

amusing ☐   happy ☐   jubilantly ☐   celebration ☐   ☐

1 mark

2 Specifically, what relation is Helen to Philip?

.... ☐

1 mark

3 What had Philip and Helen been doing before they arrived back at their house?

....

1 mark

4 Which **four** adjectives are used in the text to describe the pony in the second paragraph?

....

1 mark

5 Why do you think the author repeatedly uses the word *little* in the first paragraph?

....

1 mark

6 Why is Philip suspicious of the interaction between Helen and the man?

....

1 mark

7 What does Philip think about his relationship with Helen? Use at least **two** pieces of evidence from the text to support your answer.

....

....

....

....

2 marks

Total marks .... Time taken ....

Test 17

Extract from *The Spook's Apprentice* by Joseph Delaney

Tom has been selected to be the Spook's Apprentice, an important role in the county, protecting people from witches, boggarts, ghasts and ghosts. As part of his training, Tom has been taken by the Spook to an abandoned house.

The Spook halted outside the very last house. It was the one on the corner closest to the warehouse, the only house in the street to have a number. That number was crafted out of metal and nailed to the door. It was thirteen, the worst and unluckiest of all numbers, and directly above was a street sign high on the wall, hanging from a single rusty rivet and pointing almost vertically towards the cobbles. It said, Watery Lane.

This house did have windowpanes but the lace curtains were yellow and hung with cobwebs. This must be the haunted house my master had warned me about.

The Spook pulled a key from his pocket, unlocked the door and led the way into the darkness within. At first I was just glad to be out of the drizzle, but when he lit a candle and positioned it on the floor near the middle of the small front room, I knew that I'd be more comfortable in an abandoned cow shed. There wasn't a single item of furniture to be seen, just a bare flagged floor and heap of dirty straw under the window. The room was damp too, the air very dank and cold, and by the light of the flickering candle I could see my breath steaming.

What I saw was bad enough, but what he said was even worse.

"Well, lad, I've got business to attend to so I'll be off, but I'll be back later. Know what you have to do?"

"No, sir," I replied, watching the flickering candle, worried that it might go out at any second.

"Well, it's what I told you earlier. Weren't you listening? You need to be alert, not dreaming. Anyway, it's nothing very difficult," he explained, scratching at his beard as if there was something crawling about in it. "You just have to spend the night alone here. I bring all my new apprentices to this old house on their first night so I can find out what they're made of. Oh, but there's one thing I haven't told you. At midnight I expect you to go down into the cellar and face whatever it is that's lurking there. Cope with that and you're well on your way to being taken on permanently. Any questions?"

I had questions all right but I was too scared to hear the answers. So I just shook my head and tried to keep my top lip from trembling.

---

1   **Find** and **copy one** word that tells you what the weather is like.

....

1 mark

2   Where does the narrator say he would rather be?

....

1 mark

---

3   What does the word *dank* mean as it is used in the third paragraph?

dry ☐   still ☐   warm ☐   moist ☐

1 mark

---

4   *I had questions all right but I was too scared to hear the answers.*
What does this tell you about how the narrator is feeling?

....

....

1 mark

---

5   **Find** and **copy** a sentence that explains why they are at the house.

....

....

....

1 mark

---

6   How does the author build the suspense throughout this extract?
Mention **three** pieces of evidence from the text.

....

....

....

....

....

....

3 marks

Total marks ....   Time taken ....

Extract from *Minnow on the Say* by Philippa Pearce

Adam and David have discovered a boat, the Minnow, and a mysterious clue that leads to lost treasure. Believing they have solved the riddle, the boys are crossing the river on a bridge created by a fallen tree, when they became aware of voices.

'Andrew!' she cried, 'this is a most disagreeable place. A spider has just dropped on me.'

'Not a spider, dear – a leaf,' replied Andrew tranquilly. They were silent again, and now David felt only the burnings of his curiosity. He still could not see Andrew at all, and still could not imagine what he was doing. Suddenly, the woman in the punt spoke again, revealing that, even while being able to see Andrew, she shared David's curiosity.

'Andrew!' she cried, with a kind of timid exasperation, as she dropped her knitting into her lap. 'Will you tell me what you're doing?'

'Looking.'

'At what?'

'Just at the Codlings' place.'

David caught his breath, both at what he had heard and at the sudden pain of Adam's nails digging into the flesh of his ankle. More startling still was the woman's next remark.

'Once – yes; twice, even – I could understand it; but again and again every summer, to punt your way up here and then just stop and stare – there can be no sense in it, surely.'

'Sense? Sense?' David could hear from the man's voice that he was quite undisturbed in his reverie by this criticism. After a pause, David heard him sigh and whisper to himself: 'There might be some sense in it, some day, somehow.'

There was the sound of effort in his voice on the last word. The punt-pole had been brought into use again, and the punt moved forward downstream. The woman was looking at her knitting again, and the man was still gazing into the Codlings' woodland; neither looked back to the fallen tree, where, from the dull brown and green of the ivy, rounded eyes still stared out, until the punt and its occupants were beyond sight.

Adam and David did not speak until they were both on their own bank again; even then, there was at first a long and thoughtful silence.

'I saw that punt when I first came up in the Minnow,' said David at last. 'The people weren't in her then.'

'They live in one of the houses with gardens that go down to the river.'

'Who are they?'

'Their name is Smith – at least they say it is.'

1   What does the word *tranquilly* mean as it is used in the second paragraph?

....

1 mark

2   What do you think a 'punt' is?

....

1 mark

3   *"Their name is Smith – at least they say it is."*
What does this imply that Adam thinks about the people in the punt?

....

1 mark

4   **Find** and **copy one** word that shows the lady is frustrated or irritated by Andrew's behaviour.

....

1 mark

5   *"There might be some sense in it, some day, somehow."*
There was the sound of effort in his voice on the last word.
What **two** things does this tell you about Andrew's plans?

....

....

2 marks

6   What do you think David and Adam think about what they have seen and heard? Explain your answer in full using at least **one** piece of evidence from the text.

....

....

....

2 marks

Total marks ....   Time taken ....

Test 19

'I Saw Three Witches'

I saw three witches
That bowed down like barley,
And took to their brooms 'neath a louring sky,
And, mounting a storm-cloud,
Aloft on its margin,
Stood black in the silver as up they did fly.

I saw three witches
That mocked the poor sparrows
They carried in cages of wicker along,
Till a hawk from his eyrie
Swooped down like an arrow,
And smote on the cages, and ended their song.

I saw three witches
That sailed in a shallop,
All turning their heads with a truculent smile,
Till a bank of green osiers
Concealed their grim faces,
Though I heard them lamenting for many a mile.

I saw three witches
Asleep in a valley,
Their heads in a row, like stones in a flood,
Till the moon, creeping upward,
Looked white through the valley,
And turned them to bushes in bright scarlet bud.

Walter Ramal

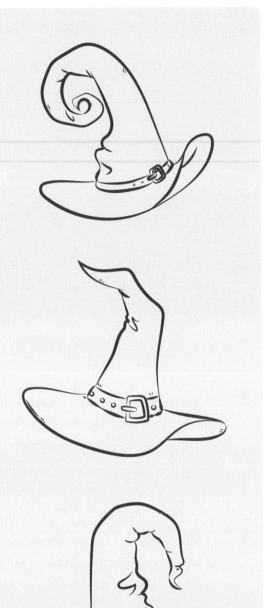

1   What **two** things do the witches do at the beginning of the poem?

1) ....

2) ....

2 marks

2   What happens to the sparrows at the end of the second verse?

....

1 mark

3 In your own words, describe what happens to the witches in the final verse.

....

....

1 mark

4 *Swooped down like an arrow*

What does this tell you about how the hawk flew? Mention **two** things.

....

1 mark

5 *Concealed their grim faces*

What does this mean?

....

1 mark

6 Draw lines to match the words from the poem to their meanings.

Look at how the words are used in the poem to help you.

lamenting	boat
louring	hit hard
eyrie	moaning
smote	nest
shallop	dark and threatening

2 marks

Total marks .... Time taken ....

Test **20**

The Water Cycle

Water is important for all life on Earth, but did you know that we only have a limited amount of it? Have you ever thought about where our water comes from and what happens to it? The water cycle (or hydrological cycle) is the natural process of the recycling of water, which is constantly happening around us. It comprises three main processes: evaporation, condensation and precipitation.

Evaporation occurs when the heat from the sun warms the water on the Earth, such as that in lakes, seas and oceans, transforming it from its liquid state to a vapour which rises up through the Earth's atmosphere. Transpiration also occurs, with the water from plants and trees evaporating from microscopic pores in leaves in a process similar to evaporation, again caused by solar energy.

The water vapour cools as it rises and this causes it to return to its liquid state or sometimes freeze into tiny ice crystals. This part of the cycle is the condensation process. The water droplets then create clouds. There are many different types of clouds, including cirrus, cumulus and nimbostratus. The different types have different appearances, caused by the density and size of the water droplets which form them.

Once the clouds become too heavy with water, precipitation occurs. This can be in the form of rain, sleet, hail or snow. The water that comes back to the Earth falls into the lakes and oceans or on to the land. The water on the land gets absorbed by the ground in a process known as infiltration, providing essential hydration for plants and trees.

This cycle is continuous; however, it can change. The melting of the polar icecaps is currently happening at a rate faster than precipitation can replace it, leading to diminishing icecaps and rising sea levels. Many people believe this is being caused by human-made global warming, which could lead to a continuing adjustment to the natural water cycle and to life on Earth.

1   According to the text, how many main processes are involved in the water cycle? Tick **one**.

two ☐   three ☐   four ☐   five ☐   ☐

1 mark

2 Which **four** forms of precipitation are mentioned in the text?

1) ....

2) ....

3) ....

4) ....

1 mark

3 Draw lines to match the word to the definition. Use the explanations in the text to help you.

| hydrological | • | • | water being soaked up by the land |

| condensation | • | • | water changing from a liquid to a gas |

| evaporation | • | • | water changing from a gas to a liquid |

| infiltration | • | • | water-related |

2 marks

4 Look at the opening paragraph. Why do you think the writer has chosen to include questions here?

....

1 mark

5 Look at the paragraph beginning *Once the clouds become too heavy...* What is the meaning of the word *hydration* as it is used in this sentence?

....

1 mark

6 Look at the final paragraph. What effect on the reader do you think the writer wants it to have? Mention **two** things

....

....

....

2 marks

Total marks ....   Time taken ....

Test **21**

Extract from *The Errand Boy* by Horatio Alger Jr.

Phil Brent was plodding through the snow in the direction of the house where he lived with his step-mother and her son, when a snow-ball, moist and hard, struck him just below his ear with stinging emphasis. The pain was considerable, and Phil's anger rose.

He turned suddenly, his eyes flashing fiercely, intent upon discovering who had committed this outrage, for he had no doubt that it was intentional.

He looked in all directions, but saw no one except a mild old gentleman in spectacles, who appeared to have some difficulty in making his way through the obstructed street.

Phil did not need to be told that it was not the old gentleman who had taken such an unwarrantable liberty with him. So he looked farther, but his ears gave him the first clue.

He heard a chuckling laugh, which seemed to proceed from behind the stone wall that ran along the roadside.

"I will see who it is," he decided, and plunging through the snow he surmounted the wall, in time to see a boy of about his own age running away across the fields as fast as the deep snow would allow.

"So it's you, Jonas!" he shouted wrathfully. "I thought it was some sneaking fellow like you."

Jonas Webb, his step-brother, his freckled face showing a degree of dismay, for he had not calculated on discovery, ran the faster, but while fear winged his steps, anger proved the more effectual spur, and Phil overtook him after a brief run, from the effects of which both boys panted.

"What made you throw that snow-ball?" demanded Phil angrily, as he seized Jonas by the collar and shook him.

"You let me alone!" said Jonas, struggling ineffectually in his grasp.

"Answer me! What made you throw that snow-ball?" demanded Phil, in a tone that showed he did not intend to be trifled with.

"Because I chose to," answered Jonas, his spite getting the better of his prudence. "Did it hurt you?" he continued, his eyes gleaming with malice.

1   **Find** and **copy one** example of **alliteration** in the second paragraph.

....

1 mark

2 What evidence is there that the old gentleman in spectacles did not throw the snowball? Mention **two** things.

....

....

1 mark

3 *"You let me alone!" said Jonas, struggling **ineffectually** in his grasp.* Which of the following words is closest in meaning to *ineffectually*?

Tick **one**.

effectively ☐   feebly ☐   angrily ☐   efficiently ☐

1 mark

4 According to the text, how many people live in Phil Brent's house?

....

1 mark

5 **Find** and **copy one** word that means the same as 'angrily'.

....

1 mark

6 What impressions do you get of Jonas Webb? Give **two** impressions, using evidence from the text to support your answer.

Impression	Evidence
	....
....	....
	....
	....
....	....
	....

3 marks

Total marks ....   Time taken ....

Test 22

Extract from *Pygmalion* by George Bernard Shaw

Act I

Covent Garden at 11.15 p.m. Torrents of heavy summer rain. Cab whistles blowing frantically in all directions. Pedestrians running for shelter into the market and under the portico of St Paul's Church, where there are already several people, among them a lady and her daughter in evening dress. They are all peering out gloomily at the rain, except one man with his back turned to the rest, who seems wholly preoccupied with a notebook in which he is writing busily.

The church clock strikes the first quarter.

THE DAUGHTER [in the space between the central pillars, close to the one on her left] I'm getting chilled to the bone. What can Freddy be doing all this time? He's been gone twenty minutes.

THE MOTHER [on her daughter's right] Not so long. But he ought to have got us a cab by now.

A BYSTANDER [on the lady's right] He won't get no cab not until half-past eleven, missus, when they come back after dropping their theatre fares.

THE MOTHER. But we must have a cab. We can't stand here until half-past eleven. It's too bad.

THE BYSTANDER. Well, it ain't my fault, missus.

THE DAUGHTER. If Freddy had a bit of gumption, he would have got one at the theatre door.

THE MOTHER. What could he have done, poor boy?

THE DAUGHTER. Other people got cabs. Why couldn't he?

Freddy rushes in out of the rain from the Southampton Street side, and comes between them closing a dripping umbrella. He is a young man of twenty, in evening dress, very wet around the ankles.

THE DAUGHTER. Well, haven't you got a cab?

FREDDY. There's not one to be had for love or money.

THE MOTHER. Oh, Freddy, there must be one. You can't have tried.

THE DAUGHTER. It's too tiresome. Do you expect us to go and get one ourselves?

FREDDY. I tell you they're all engaged. The rain was so sudden: nobody was prepared; and everybody had to take a cab. I've been to Charing Cross one way and nearly to Ludgate Circus the other; and they were all engaged.

THE MOTHER. Did you try Trafalgar Square?

FREDDY. There wasn't one at Trafalgar Square.

THE DAUGHTER. Did you try?

FREDDY. I tried as far as Charing Cross Station. Did you expect me to walk to Hammersmith?

THE DAUGHTER. You haven't tried at all.

THE MOTHER. You really are very helpless, Freddy. Go again; and don't come back until you have found a cab.

1 *There's not one to be had for love or money.* What does Freddy mean by this?

The cabs are very expensive. ☐   It is impossible to get a cab. ☐

There are no cabs to be seen. ☐   He refuses to try to find a cab. ☐   ☐

1 mark

2 Why are they struggling to get a cab?

.... ☐

1 mark

3 Tick each statement to say whether it is **true** or **false**.

	True	False
Freddy is thirty years old.		
The scene takes place in Covent Garden.		
It is summertime.		
The lady, her daughter and Freddy are smartly dressed.		

☐

1 mark

4 **Find** and **copy one** word that means 'initiative'.

.... ☐

1 mark

5 Think about the features of a script. Why does some text appear in brackets?

....

.... ☐

1 mark

6 What do the mother and daughter think of Freddy's efforts to get a cab? Explain your answer in full, referring to at least **two** pieces of evidence from the text.

....

....

.... ☐

3 marks

Total marks ....   Time taken ....

Progress chart

Write the score (out of 8) for each test in the box provided to the right of the chart.
Then colour the row next to the box to represent this score.

								Total
Test 1								
Test 2								
Test 3								
Test 4								
Test 5								
Test 6								
Test 7								
Test 8								
Test 9								
Test 10								
Test 11								
Test 12								
Test 13								
Test 14								
Test 15								
Test 16								
Test 17								
Test 18								
Test 19								
Test 20								
Test 21								
Test 22								

1   2   3   4   5   6   7   8

Score (out of 8)